The Curse of the Mummy

Special tips for detectives assigned to work in:

Country name: **EGYPT**

- Remember the influence of religion, particularly on Friday, the sabbath. This is the day of rest, when all offices are closed in this area.
- The presidency is powerful and President Sadat imposed respect for mummies as the remains of dead ancestors.
- Superstition can be strong, particularly around the tombs of the Pharaohs.

Metropolitan Police Form 459/OS344/D994

Instructions to Detective Solomon Jolly and partner for Egyptian assignment:

1. Examine all evidence carefully, looking for revealing remarks made in interviews and any clues in photographs. Take careful note of the X-ray.
2. Look particularly for faked documents; a faulty typewriter may be a giveaway.
3. Remember, not everyone is who or what they seem.
4. As French police say: *Cherchez la femme* (look for a love motive).

The British Embassy - Cairo, Egypt

Office of the Deputy First Secretary

Fax Message: 19 44 171 666 00041

Date : April 1st 1996
To : The Foreign & Commonwealth Office, Whitehall, England.

Attn : Middle East desk

Attempted theft of valuable mummy cartonnage at Cairo airport. The suspect is English. Egyptian police request urgent London police attendance.

FOREIGN & COMMONWEALTH OFFICE

Downing Street
LONDON SW1A 2AL

Date: April 2nd 1996

FAX MESSAGE 0171 666 888 4456

To: Private Secretary, Home Secretary
From: Private Secretary, Foreign & Commonwealth Secretary

Egyptian police seeking urgent assistance in matter of attempted theft of mummy cartonnage at Cairo airport. Prime Minister feels British Museum exhibition will be ruined if prize exhibit delayed. Send assistance immediately.

Consulate General of EGYPT

Visa No.: 9833/34 Date: 2/4/96
Name: Detective Solomon Jolly
Expiry Date: 2/5/96
Duration: ONE MONTH
Number of entries: ONE
Reason for travel: Police Investigator
Dues collected: £28 —
The Consul General: [signature]

OPITB4 TYPE C

****

PASSENGER TICKET AND BAGGAGE CHECK
SUBJECT TO CONDITIONS OF CONTRACT

DATE OF ISSUE
03 APR 96 PASSENGER RECEIPT 1 OF 1

ISSUED BY
EGYPT AIRLINES

PLACE OF ISSUE
BOND ST

NAME OF PASSENGER/NOT TRANSFERABLE
JOLLY/S MR

FARE
GBP £550

FORM OF PAYMENT
CASH

STOCK CONTROL NUMBER
9764839 474992206
DO NOT MARK OR WRITE IN THE WHITE AREA ABOVE

PASSENGER COUPON

NAME OF PASSENGER/NOT TRANSFERABLE
JOLLY/S MR

FROM
LONDON LHR
EA 377
CLUB CLASS

TO
CAIRO CA1

GATE
12

BOARD TIME
0700 HRS

SEAT
3C NO SMOKING

STOCK CONTROL NUMBER
9764839 474992206

REPORT

Date: April 3rd 1996
Time: 4.35 p.m.
By Detective Superintendent Solomon Jolly

Acting on instructions received, I flew to Egypt and attended at Cairo Airport air cargo building, where I was briefed by Lieutenant Mahfouz of the Egyptian Police department. There was a large presence of armed officers. Inside the customs interview room, resting on a table, was an ornate coffin of the type known as a mummy cartonnage.

The cartonnage was covered in gold, inlaid with ivory, mother-of-pearl and many precious stones. You did not need to be an expert in Egyptology to see that this relic of the Pharaohs, perhaps 4,000 years old, was priceless. Lieutenant Mahfouz informed me that there had been a daring and ingenious attempt to divert the cartonnage from the British Museum exhibition and sell it, a crime punishable by at least four years' imprisonment.

I said that it was imperative that its delivery not be delayed; it was to be the prime exhibit, and the exhibition was due to open in five days. Lieutenant Mahfouz replied by pointing at the machinery mounted over the cartonnage. It was an X-ray apparatus. Customs officers had obtained a picture of what appeared to be the actual mummy inside. For some reason, the sight of the X-ray picture had caused a wave of fear and panic to rush through the cargo building.

Lieutenant Mahfouz then showed me an air waybill from the Cargo Globe company and a letter from an Egyptian Immigration Officer. This evidence, according to Lieutenant Mahfouz, proved that the criminal was, without doubt, English. I urged him to calm his colleagues, who seemed terrified that the mummy bore some kind of curse, and to have the precious cartonnage opened for inspection.

STAPLE DOCUMENTS ABOVE PERFORATION

Shipper's name and address: The Museum of Egyptian Antiquities, Cairo.	Acc. no: EM1
Consignee's name and address: The British Museum, London, England.	Cons. Acc No: 4356
Issuing Carrier's Agent Name and City: Mahmoud Muharram Cairo, Egypt	
IATA: 89J5	Acc No: MM565

Not negotiable

AIR WAYBILL

(Air consignment note)

CARGO GLOBE

Accounting Info: Pre-paid

By	Declared value	
1st carrier	$205,000,000 US	
Airport destination	**Flight date**	**Amount of insurance**
London Heathrow	31 Mar 96	$205,000,000 US.

Handling information

Weight 82.5kg

VERY URGENT HIGH PRIORITY
PRECIOUS GOODS - HANDLE WITH EXTREME CARE

Nature and Quantity of Goods

ARCHAEOLOGICAL EXHIBIT FROM ROOM 52 AT THE MUSEUM OF EGYPTIAN ANTIQUITIES
ONE GILDED CARTONNAGE INLAID WITH JEWELS
ONE MUMMIFIED HUMAN CADAVER
The whole paper-wrapped in a wooden crate

Prepaid weight charge	Other charges
Calculated at UK £275/kg	Express premium UK £3,500
Signature of shipper	**Shipper certifies details herein exact**
Lord Letherburn	Lord Letherburn

STATEMENT
by Lieutenant Mahfouz
Date: April 3rd 1996
Time: 5.30 p.m.
Taken by Detective Superintendent Solomon Jolly

I was called to Cairo airport cargo building in Heliopolis by customs officials on March 31st 1996 and took note of a richly-decorated cartonnage surrounded by its discarded wooden freight packaging.

I examined an air waybill which showed that the Museum of Egyptian Antiquities was transporting the mummy, valued at 205 million dollars to the British Museum as an 'archaeological exhibit for loan'. The waybill was signed by Lord Letherburn, the distinguished archaeological adviser to the Museum of Egyptian Antiquities.

I took note of the actual weight of the mummy and cartonnage – 202.6 kilograms, as against the chargeable weight of 82.5 kilograms written on the waybill. This difference in weight had aroused the customs officers' suspicions, so I ordered an X-ray photograph to be taken.

The X-ray revealed a bizarre sight – a human skeleton, with what appeared to be cylinders of some kind on either side of it. The sight caused several officials to collapse in apparent terror, shouting 'The Pilot of Darkness! The Pilot of Darkness!'. An uproar spread throughout the building. Some staff told me they thought the cylinders were bombs – but many more referred to 'The Curse of Alemcolet'. I recognised the name of this notorious curse, known throughout our land, and had to steel my nerves.

After summoning armed troops, I telephoned Lord Letherburn at 11.35 a.m. at his hotel in Cairo and he confirmed that his assistant, Mr. Quentin Root, had disappeared after acting suspiciously, during the week of March 18th 1996. He copied to me a letter from the Egyptian Department of the Interior ordering the arrest of Mr Root, who had not renewed his permit to stay in Egypt. He also passed us a memo that Root slipped under his hotel door, long before his disappearance.

Closer examination of the X-ray has now confirmed that the cartonnage contains, not an Egyptian mummy, but a recently-deceased human body. Judging from the description, I can only conclude that the body is Quentin Root's. In an ingenious attempt to steal the cartonnage, he must have got rid of of the original mummy, installed himself inside the cartonnage at the last minute and equipped himself with scuba tanks and enough air supply to reach London Heathrow airport. This is where he intended to emerge and steal the cartonnage to sell on the black market. Somehow his plan was foiled and he suffocated during the delay.

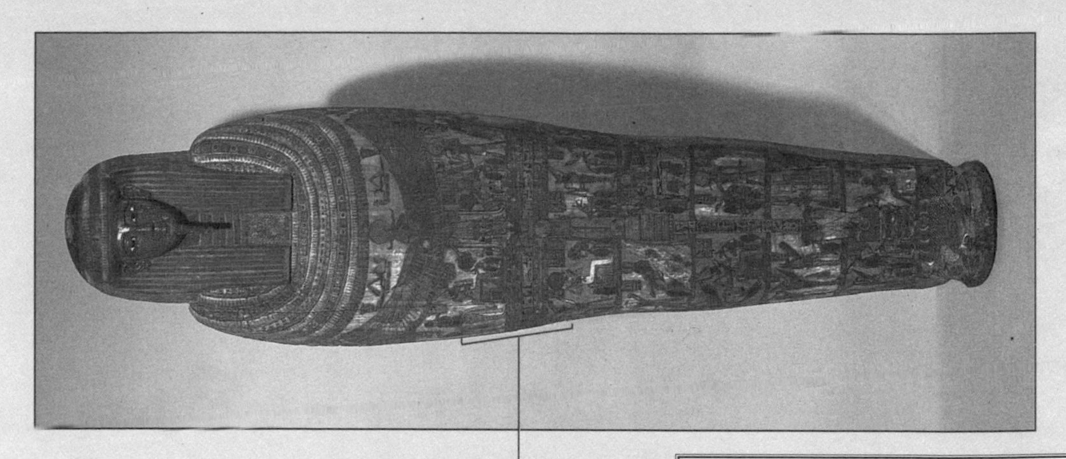

Photograph of cartonnage taken at Cairo airport - April 3rd 1996
Police photographic evidence no. 5912/A

Close-up of image on side of cartonnage - 'The Curse of Alemcolet'.
Police photographic evidence no. 5912/B

ARAB REPUBLIC of EGYPT

Department of the Interior

Maydan al tahrir

Cairo

Friday, Mar h 29th 1996

Lord Letherburn
Nile Hilton Hotel

Esteemed Lordship

Mr. QUENTIN ROOT
United Kingdom National
Passport Number: 6588459J

The above person entered the A.R.E. on a 90-day permit, which is now six days overdue for renewal. I hereby inform you, as his registered employer, that he is now listed as missing, and I have issued orders for him to be arrested as soon as possible, and held in ustody for questioning.

Respe tfully yours

Ahmed Malban
Inspe tor of Immigration

REPORT
Date: April 4th 1996
Time: 5.45 p.m.
By Detective Superintendent Solomon Jolly

An hour ago, technicians wearing oxygen masks from the Department of Antiquities cut open the cartonnage. The vile smell confirmed my opinion that the body would be beyond recognition. The high, dry temperature at which mummies are normally stored has aggravated the body's rapid decay. Identification of bodies can usually be made from dental records, showing fillings and other dental work. In this case, however, the teeth of the corpse show no work, therefore positive identification from dental records cannot be expected.

We know Quentin Root was a young archaeologist, promoted to an important position by his employer, Lord Letherburn. On the brink of a major discovery, he suddenly disappeared. Now human remains corresponding to his description have been discovered inside a cartonnage of immense value.

The cartonnage itself has been examined and it is now clear that it is not the one intended for the British Museum exhibition. It is a completely different cartonnage – and it is one which appears to bear a curse. Clearly, this matter needs further investigation.

I endorse Lieutenant Mahfouz's view that the corpse is Root's, but do not think he was engaged in a reckless scheme to steal the mummy on arrival at Heathrow airport. The air tanks attached to the body have been found to be completely empty and therefore useless. It is difficult to believe that Root could have worked out such an elaborate scheme to steal the mummy, only to forget to put any air in his scuba tanks. Medical reports have found that there is a depression on the skull, showing that a wound had recently been received to the head. This is more likely to have been the cause of death.

This so-called 'theft' has clearly been set up. I am now convinced that, in addition to being an attempted theft, this is a case of murder – the murder of Quentin Root.

Mahmoud Muharram 6/4/96
Photographic evidence no. 5912/U

<u>INTERVIEW</u>
with Mahmoud Muharram
Date: April 6th 1996
Conducted and tape-recorded at 10.15 a.m. by
Detective Superintendent Solomon Jolly.

<u>JOLLY</u>: Mr Muharram, I believe you are a dealer in antiquities.

<u>MUHARRAM</u>: I am. Licensed, legal and above board.

<u>JOLLY</u>: When did you last see Quentin Root?

<u>MUHARRAM</u>: Early in the morning on Lord Letherburn's dig in the first dynasty tombs at Saqqara, exactly a week ago today. I remember it well, because he had wanted to see me the day before, and I had to remind him how little happens in Egypt on our sabbath, your Friday.

<u>JOLLY</u>: He'd invited you? Why?

<u>MUHARRAM</u>: For an excellent reason. He had opened in total secrecy the tomb of Prince Alemcolet. It was the find of a lifetime: just one cartonnage, resting in an empty chamber, but a cartonnage so outstanding that on its own it was worth more than 200 million dollars.

<u>JOLLY</u>: An unrobbed tomb? Is that not extremely rare, in fact, virtually unknown?

<u>MUHARRAM</u>: I did not say it had not been robbed. Over thousands of years it had been robbed of all its treasures, all except the cursed mummy itself, encased in its priceless cartonnage.

<u>JOLLY</u>: Strange, such a precious mummy never being stolen.

<u>MUHARRAM</u>: But not so strange to us, Detective Jolly. I stood in the tomb, knowing that the Curse of Alemcolet had protected these remains since the dawn of time. The mummy lying alone, untouchable, for nearly thirty centuries, was shocking proof.

<u>JOLLY</u>: What did Mr Root want? A valuation?

<u>MUHARRAM</u>: I believe so but I found it difficult to understand him. He was ghastly pale, trembling, hardly able to speak. He seemed to want to know more about the curse. I had visited his dig many times previously. He had been a brilliant young man with a bright future. Now, he resembled a ghost, as if the immense value of his find had no meaning at all, except death.

Continued over...

JOLLY: And what about you? You deal in such things. You must have thought of the money.

MUHARRAM: As a licensed dealer I was staring at a share in a huge fortune, but the power of the curse was so strong, I could only blabber one thing again and again, like a man bewitched: 'Room 52, Room 52'.

JOLLY: What is 'Room 52'?

MUHARRAM: The secret room at our Museum of Egyptian Antiquities, where the remains of the powerful are given peace and respect, the only place where a curse can be laid to rest.

JOLLY: The curse obviously upset you, but I refuse to believe that you lost your business instinct. I believe you decided at that moment to get hold of the mummy and cartonnage yourself and sell it abroad for millions. And for good measure you, a large man, overcame Mr Root, killed him, and shipped him out with the loot, setting him up for the theft and keeping the secret with you alone.

MUHARRAM: You are accusing me of murder?

JOLLY: So, you admit the theft?

MUHARRAM: Impossible! Our beloved President Sadat forbade the disrespectful display of the dead, and I would never risk the Curse of Alemcolet. Far from threatening anyone, I myself am in deadly danger, simply by having laid eyes on the Curse of Alemcolet with its dreaded cartouche, one that has terrified bold thieves for thousands of years. I wish I had never gone to vault 3Y, I wish I had never seen Mr Root...

(Interview terminated by Detective Jolly due to suspect's distress.)

The ghafir at Saqqara 6/4/96
Police photographic evidence no. 6012/D

STATEMENT
of ghafir (watchman) of 1st dynasty tombs at Saqqara
Date: April 6th 1996
Time: 2.30 p.m.
Taken by Detective Superintendent Solomon Jolly, with Lieutenant Mahfouz as interpreter.
(A baksheesh of £50 was paid.)

GHAFIR: Mr Root fix three new, heavy padlocks on tomb a week ago, Saturday, birthday of my camel. He do job himself. All workers at dig site are dismissed same day. Treasure was expected behind wall, but he tell workers nothing. They just sacked when they arrive in morning. Told go home. They very suspicious. Then other man come to see him, Egyptian man with moustache.

Mr Root give me a copy of the keys because I trusted. I work here twenty years. Everyone know me. Unlike workers, I not hate Mr Root.

I never open vault since then. I not want Curse of Alemcolet, like him. Yes, Mr Root look very sick after. Skin like sand, face hairy, eyes like thunder. Twenty years older. Pilot of Darkness, he turning Mr Root's dreams to nightmare.

I never open vault until you order me now. But you see this piece of stone – carries sign of curse. Terrible things happen to all who disrespect the remains of Alemcolet, son of Zoser the Pharaoh. Alemcolet's Pilot of Darkness enters their dreams at night. See him, here? Pilot come from dark star in sky, has black wings of power for flying into your heart and bringing nightmare. You dream bad, bad things. Your skin wrinkles, your hair is thin, you age many years in a few days. Then you wake up dead.

Yes, Mr Root was here seven days ago. I see him later on same day with milord (Lord Letherburn), in Land Rover. I saw milord driving away later, but he not with Mr Root. Is Mr Root dead yet? He will not live for long. Curse kill everybody, some slow, some quick. But it come to everybody. Even to esteemed policemen.

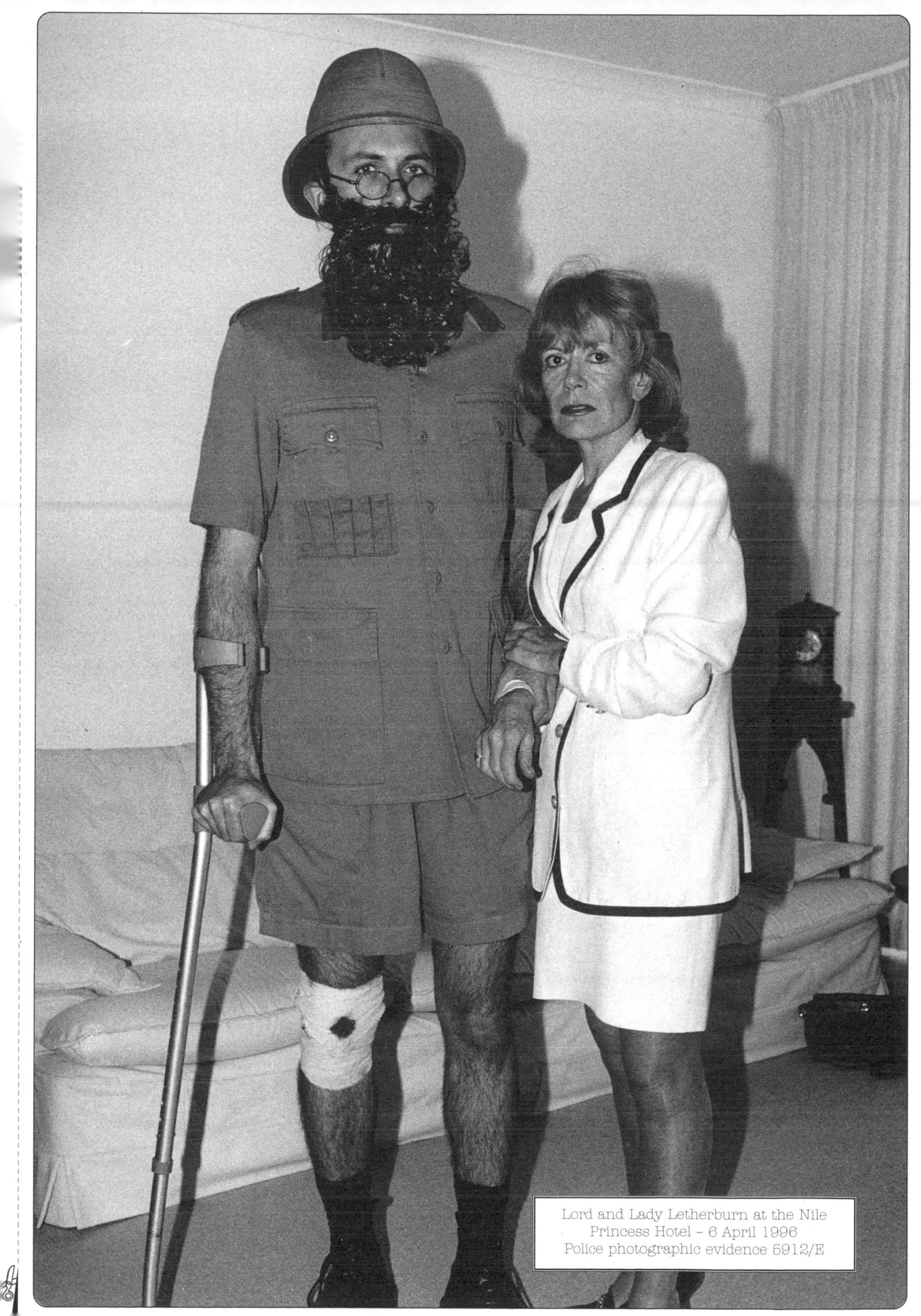
Lord and Lady Letherburn at the Nile
Princess Hotel – 6 April 1996
Police photographic evidence 5912/E

INTERVIEW with Lady Letherburn
Date: April 6th 1996
Conducted at 7.15 p.m. by Detective Superintendent Solomon Jolly

JOLLY: Thank you for waiting, Your Ladyship. I would like to ask you a few questions about Mr Quentin Root.

HER LADYSHIP: I never met him while he was alive, or any of the other dig staff. I spend every winter deep-sea diving in the Red Sea, and these last six weeks I have been nursing my husband, who has been laid up with a bad injury to his left leg. He insists on climbing all over those horrid ruins.

JOLLY: You have no interest in archaeology?

HER LADYSHIP: My husband is the genius at archaeology. My interest lies with different rocks, those made by a marine invertebrate of the class Anthozoa in the phylum Cnidaria in their relationship with microscopic algae. I refer, of course, to coral reefs.

JOLLY: Does your husband like to scuba dive, too?

HER LADYSHIP: With a passion, but he is too busy.

JOLLY: Your Ladyship, when I first mentioned Mr Root, you assumed he was dead.

HER LADYSHIP: Didn't you mention it?

JOLLY: No, and I have a newspaper clipping here with a photograph of Mr Root and yourself. You were clearly looking round the dig, and the pair of you look very fond of each other. You have your arm around him.

HER LADYSHIP: Yes, I see. Well, it was a very brief visit. I must have forgotten. Digs bore me so. As for my arm being around him, I can assure you that his arm was around me. He repelled me. I remember that after that meeting I had to have my clothes sent to the cleaners. He never took a bath.

JOLLY: I think you're making a bad job of pretending to dislike Mr Root. I think that when you visited Saqqara he told you Alemcolet would soon be discovered, and that the remains could be worth 200 million dollars. I do not think you found that information boring at all.

HER LADYSHIP: You are illogical, Detective Jolly. Why would I murder Mr Root if I wanted him to help me get 200 million dollars for his mummy?

JOLLY: I am not saying you murdered him.

HER LADYSHIP: Well, this is a mystery!

Continued over...

JOLLY: You may well have meant it to be, madam.

HER LADYSHIP: What are you suggesting?

JOLLY: You are a scuba diver, familiar with diving equipment. Root's body had scuba tanks attached. Did you supply them?

HER LADYSHIP: I'm lost. Why would I do that?

JOLLY: To help him smuggle himself out of the country. And at the same time to terrify any curious Egyptian officials, because you had noticed that the Curse of Alemcolet includes a figure called the Pilot of Darkness, which appears to have tanks on its back.

HER LADYSHIP: This is all outrageous. I will say nothing more until I consult my solicitor.

The Egyptian News

Egyptian News 26 February 1996

Exciting finds expected in Saqqara tomb search

Dramatic discoveries are expected in Lord Letherburn's three-year-old dig in the first dynasty sector.

Newly-appointed dig manager Quentin Root, 24, said at a news conference yesterday that signs of a concealed entrance had been found at the end of Vault 3Y, believed to lead to the resting place of Prince Alemcolet, one of the sons of the ancient King Zoser.

'Site evidence and detailed research suggests that we could be investigating a tomb which has never been robbed,' Mr Root said. 'Alemcolet's mummy and funeral treasures could be just a few weeks' digging away.'

Mr Root said he was not at all worried by the uncovering of the notorious cartouche, traditionally reputed to depict the curse of Alemcolet. This contains a figure known in Egypt as the 'Pilot of Darkness'. The cartouche is recorded in ancient texts, and was first discovered carved on the wall of the tomb of King Zoser. Lord Letherburn himself was unable to comment as his recurrent leg injury prevented his attendance of the news conference.

Quentin Root and Lady Letherburn at the dig yesterday.

President of Egypt

Saqqara Diggings Ltd

Memorandum

```
To: Lord Letherburn          From: Quentin Root
Re: Dig progress             Date: 27th February 1996
```

So sorry to hear about your leg injury from Lady Letherburn. Everything is going extremely well here and we think we're on the verge of a very ex iting find on the site.

All best for a speedy re overy

Quentin Root

INTERVIEW

with Lord Letherburn

Date: April 6th 1996

Time: 9.00 p.m.

Conducted by Detective Superintendent Solomon Jolly

JOLLY: Your Lordship, do you employ Mr Quentin Root as your dig manager at Saqqara?

HIS LORDSHIP: I do, he is one of several managers overseeing my explorations all over Egypt, at Luxor, Abydos and the Valley of Kings. He is young, I hired him only in January, but he will go far.

JOLLY: He'll go no further now. I regret to inform you that I am investigating his murder.

HIS LORDSHIP: But, I don't understand. There must be some mistake.

JOLLY: I am afraid not, Your Lordship. You confirmed to police that Mr Root disappeared during the week of March 18th?

HIS LORDSHIP: Yes, indeed. But I thought Quentin might just have gone off travelling for a while. He's young – this kind of thing is to be expected.

JOLLY: Your Lordship, you and Quentin Root were seen together at Saqqara on the afternoon of Saturday 30 March. Can you confirm that you saw Mr Root that day?

HIS LORDSHIP: What are you talking about? I haven't been out for weeks. I have been kept in my hotel room with my right knee, an old dig injury. Both my wife and the hotel staff have been nursing me. You can confirm it with them.

JOLLY: You pretend not to know that the tomb of Prince Alemcolet was opened and the precious mummy found?

HIS LORDSHIP: The tomb has not been opened yet. There is a long-standing curse at Alemcolet. I ordered Root not to open it without my permission and I am sure he would not have done so. We could lose all our trained staff at Saqqara – they are terrified of the curse.

JOLLY: We know the tomb was opened because we have the cartonnage securely held at the airport.

HIS LORDSHIP: Are you sure you are not mistaking it for a valuable cartonnage from Room 52 at the Museum of Antiquities? I authorised such a cartonnage to be legally transported to London.

Continued over...

JOLLY: The cartonnage held at the airport is clearly marked with the Curse of Alemcolet. It struck terror into the customs officers and experts have clearly identified it. Perhaps you would have wished us to mistake Alemcolet's cartonnage for the one being legally exported from Room 52, your Lordship?

HIS LORDSHIP: Are you implying what I think you are, my man?

JOLLY: I am merely remarking, sir, that you deny visiting the tomb, when we have a witness who saw you there just before the cartonnage was shipped.

HIS LORDSHIP: Nonsense! Can't you see my injury? I can hardly walk!

JOLLY: Most of us could travel a few miles to look at 200 million dollars, sir. You cannot deny that it was highly convenient for you to have Quentin Root disappear, thereby keeping the secret of Alemcolet's discovery? His death cleared the way for you to sell the cartonnage on the black market. The cartonnage offered a handy way to ship his body out of the country, did it not?

HIS LORDSHIP: I'm bewildered. I have no idea what you're talking about. I refuse to speak to you any more until I have the advice of a solicitor.

REPORT

Date: April 8th 1996

by Detective Superintendent Solomon Jolly

I was sent here to investigate a case of theft. This has now turned into a bizarre murder enquiry. Now that I have interviewed all the principal suspects, I have to declare myself unable to recommend with complete confidence an arrest in the murder of Quentin Root.

Mahmoud Muhurram, dealer in antiquities

He had the opportunity of killing Quentin Root at the tomb on Saturday 30th March and stowing the body in the cartonnage. His expert knowledge of antiquities would have enabled him to sell the cartonnage on the black market and make more money than he would ever earn in his life. But surely his beliefs and fear of the Curse of Alemcolet would not allow him to touch such an important mummy?

The ghafir at the tomb

Quentin Root was disliked by all his workers at the dig and even though the ghafir denied hating Mr Root, this may not be true. He could have done it out of hatred, but, as far as we know, had no knowledge about the planned shipment of a cased mummy from the Egyptian Museum to London. As with Mahmoud Muhurram, his fear of the curse is apparent.

Lord Letherburn

If we are to believe the ghafir, Lord Letherburn was at the tomb on the afternoon of Saturday 30th March. He could have murdered Quentin Root out of jealousy (Root is obviously very close to his wife, Lady Letherburn), but, being already immensely rich, lacked a profit motive for stealing the cartonnage. He would have preferred the fame and glory of the discovery of the precious encased mummy of Prince Alemcolet – unless he wanted to keep it for his own personal collection.

Lady Letherburn

She could have persuaded Quentin Root to steal the mummy and cartonnage on her behalf – and a promise of sharing the loot. As an expert diver she could have thought of the scuba tank ruse. Root may have been double-crossed by her if she had deliberately left the air out of the scuba tanks. But there is no evidence to justify this theory.

I am at a loss, and await further instructions.

Solomon Jolly

....